HEATHCLIFF RIDES AGAIN

The funniest feline in America delights millions of fans every day as he appears in over 500 newspapers. You'll have a laugh a minute as Heathcliff tangles with the milkman, the fish store owner, the tuna fisherman and just about everyone else he runs into. If you're looking for some fun, look no further, Heathcliff is here.

HEATHCLIFF

HEATHCLIFF RIDES AGAIN
BY GEORGE GATELY

CHARTER BOOKS, NEW YORK

HEATHCLIFF RIDES AGAIN

A Charter Book / published by arrangement with
McNaught Syndicate, Inc.

PRINTING HISTORY
Thirteenth printing / January 1984

ISBN: 0-441-32401-0

Charter Books are published by The Berkley Publishing Group,
200 Madison Avenue, New York, New York 10016.
PRINTED IN THE UNITED STATES OF AMERICA

"YOU PHONED FOR AN EXTERMINATOR?"

"TAKE ME TO YOUR LEADER!"

"LOOK OUT!...DON'T GET CRUMBS IN HIS BED!"

"I'LL DO THE JUDGING, IF YOU DON'T MIND!"

"WHAT'S THIS BILL FOR FIFTY-FIVE DOLLARS FROM THE CARPENTER?...

...REPAIRS ON HEATHCLIFF'S SCRATCHING POST!!"

"I'M AFRAID YOUR CAT DOESN'T LIKE IT HERE!"

"I'LL SHOW YOU PUNKS HOW TO PLAY
FOOTBALL!...GET ME A HELMET."

"SOMEONE'S BEEN FOOLING AROUND WITH THE STUFFED BIRD EXHIBIT!"

"WOTTA YA IN FOR, KID?"

"OH, GOODNESS ME!...I SEE BABY IS HUNGRY."

"CARE FOR A CANTER THROUGH THE PARK?"

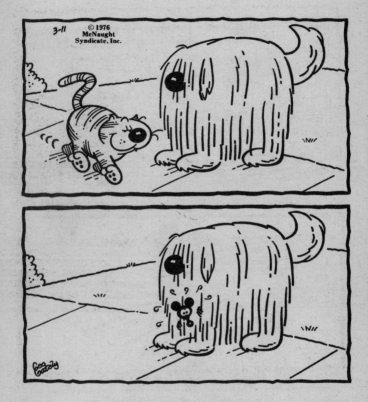

"IS HE BACK AGAIN ?!"

"YOU GAVE IT TO THE DELIVERY BOY?!!...
WE DON'T HAVE A DELIVERY BOY!!"

"JUST CATCH THEM!...DON'T TRAIN THEM!"

"OH, OH!"

"HE DOESN'T TAKE SUGAR.....
JUST LOTS AND LOTS OF CREAM!"

© 1975
McNaught Synd., Inc.

WHOOPEE CAT FOOD INC.

"LOOK WHO'S LEFT HIMSELF ON OUR DOORSTEP."

"I WAS READING HEATHCLIFF SOME OF
YOUR OLD LOVE LETTERS."

"STOP, THIEF!"

"WELL, AT LEAST HE'S A GOOD SPORT ABOUT NOT WINNING!"

"ONE OF OUR SHARKS IS MISSING!"

"I TELL YOU, HE'S IN HERE SOMEPLACE...
HIS GETAWAY CAR IS PARKED OUT FRONT!"

"ANOTHER COMPLAINT!....HE'S TANGLED WITH A
RUSSIAN WOLFHOUND!"

"THAT LITTLE FELLOW IN THE CAT SUIT WON A BUNDLE!"

"WATCH OUT!...HIS MOOD RING IS TURNING
A NASTY COLOR!"

"HE'S A GARBAGE DUMPER'S GARBAGE DUMPER!"

"BUT GRANDMA, HEATHCLIFF WON'T CHASE A MOUSE WHILE HE'S ON HIS MILK BREAK!"

"WATCH THIS GUY AND YOU'LL LEARN SOMETHING!"

"HE'S A VERY EFFICIENT MASCOT!"

"HE WON'T COME OUT... HE'S TIRED OF BEING JUST ANOTHER HANDSOME FACE."

"POOR BABY !...DID-UMS GET A BOO BOO ?"

"I'LL HANDLE THIS!"

"BONGO!...WHERE ARE YOU, BONGO ?!"

" NOW, WATCH THE BIRDIE, SON ... "

"HE'S A VERY POOR LOSER!"

"...AND INHABITED BY STRANGE, FURRY CREATURES!..."

"HE DOESN'T SEEM TO MIND A MILK BATH!"

"WELL, THAT'S SHOW BIZ!"

"LET ME IN!...LET ME IN!"

"BOOK HIM!"

"I'M NOT READY FOR YOU YET!"

"HOLD IT, WISE GUY!"

"HE'S GOT SOMEBODY NEW SINGING BASS!"

"NO THANK YOU!... I'VE ALREADY EATEN!!"

"MISS, DID YOU LOSE A MEGAPHONE?"

"COMFY?"

"DID YOU KNOW HEATHCLIFF'S GOT MONEY
IN HIS MATTRESS ?!"

"THAT'S FUNNY... I THOUGHT IT WAS *YOUR*
STOMACH RUMBLING!"

"I SAW YOU SWIPE THAT FISH!...NOW, WHERE IS IT?"

"DID I HEAR THE FLAMINGO SCREAM?!"

"SHOULD THE MASCOT DINE WITH THE TEAM?"

"HE LIKES TO BUILD A NICE WARM FIRE
ON THESE CHILLY DAYS."

"SAY!...THAT LOOKS LIKE SPIKE!...
HOW DID YOU DO THAT ?!"

"THE OCTOPUS WILL DEFEND ITSELF BY EMITTING A CLOUD OF BLACK INK."

"HE DOESN'T LIKE HIS NEW PILLS!"

"MAYBE HEATHCLIFF SHOULDN'T GO OUT
ON SUCH A COLD NIGHT!"

"THERE'S YOUR TROUBLE!"

"YOU DON'T CARE FOR 'PINKY, THE PEPPY
LITTLE PUPPY'?"

"MUGGSY FABER HIT HIM IN THE HEAD
WITH A SNOWBALL."

"*THIS* IS NOT A SCRATCHING POST!"

"MAY I HAVE A VOLUNTEER FROM THE AUDIENCE, PLEASE?"

"WHAT'S HE DOING WITH MY SNOOZE-ALARM?"

"IT'S THE ZOO... SOMETHING ABOUT A PEACOCK!"

"I COULDN'T RECOGNIZE HIM... HE HAD
A STOCKING OVER HIS FACE!"

"SCRAM, YOU PHONEY!"

"WELL, SO MUCH FOR KISSING BABIES!"

"YOU WOULDN'T BELIEVE THE STUFF HE FINDS IN A GARBAGE CAN !!"

"I DON'T THINK HE APPRECIATED YOUR LITTLE JOKE!"

"I'M MAKING A SANDWICH... DO YOU WANT
ANYTHING, HEATHCLIFF?"

"WE'RE ALL SET....NOW IF WE JUST HAD
A COSTUME FOR SPIKE!"

© 1976
McNaught
Syndicate, Inc.

"GET OUT OF THAT BIRD FEEDER!"

"WE GET AN OCCASIONAL MOUSE IN THE BASEMENT."

"YOUR CAT'S QUITE A COMEDIAN!"

"CLEAN-UP DAY."

"CUCKOO!"

"C'MON, HEATHCLIFF!... DON'T DISTURB THE BATS!"

"YOU'RE GIVING THE PLACE A BAD NAME!"

"HE GOT SOMEONE TO DO THE LYRICS!"

"WHAT HAPPENED TO ALL THE MONEY?!"

"DON'T DO ANYTHING I WOULDN'T DO!"

"HAVE YOU SEEN HEATHCLIFF?... HE WAS CHASING A SKUNK!"

"YOUR NE'ER-DO-WELL BROTHER IS AT THE DOOR."

"HE DOESN'T WANT ANY PICTURES TAKEN."

"IT'S NOT A MOUSE, HEATHCLIFF!...IT'S A CHIHUAHUA!"

4-21 © 1976
McNaught Synd., Inc.